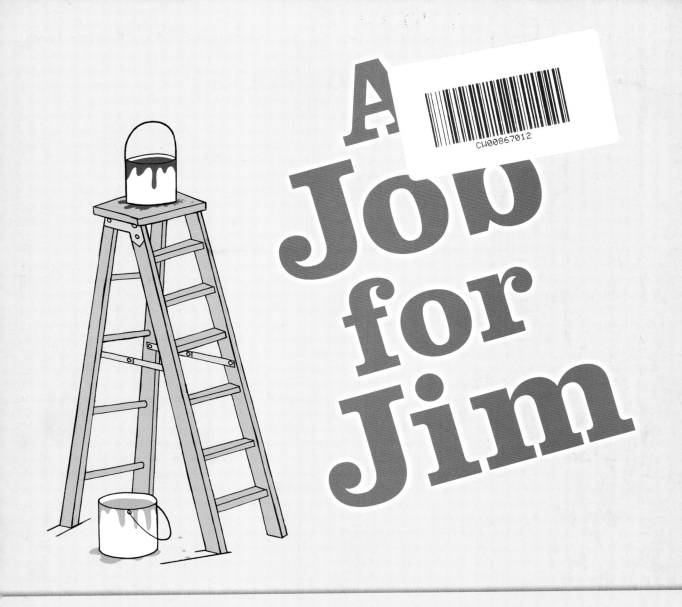

A Job for Jim

Written by Paul Shipton

Illustrated by Simon Cooper

Jim has a job in a shop.
"This is boring," thinks Jim.

2

So he looks at some job adverts.

"I like food," thinks Jim.
So he gets a job as a waiter.

But the job is much harder than he thinks.

Jim has to run up and down the stairs with lots of starters, until ...

... he drops all the food.
CRASH!

"I like fresh air," thinks Jim.
"Perhaps I will be a farmer!"

So he gets a job on a farm.

Jim is still in bed when he hears
a rooster. The sun is not up yet!

"Dear, dear," he thinks.
"This is not the job for me!"

"I was good at art when I was
a kid," thinks Jim.
So he gets a job as a painter.

But he is not too good at
this job.

Jim's boss tells him, "There is some paint in the room ...

... but a LOT of paint on you!"

The next week, Jim is back in his shop. "I like this job best of all," he thinks.